Go to the Head!

Ian is a children's poet living in Lancashire. When he isn't working on wonderful poetry books such as this one he spends his time visiting scores of primary schools, libraries and festivals all over the UK and Europe performing his poetry and leading exciting poetry workshops. Ian has appeared on BBC1's Match of the Day as Wigan Athletic's Poet in Residence, a job he continues to love.

Ian is married to Kathryn and together they have five year old twins James and Madeleine.

For a fun day of poetry and all round creativity you can contact Ian at **www.ianbland.com**.

So There!

The other contributor, Phil,
Is hoping his stuff fits the bill,
But if you think it's guff
He's inclined to say, 'tough!'
(Cos his mum thinks his poetry's brill.)

Also by Ian Bland and Philip Waddell

A BUG IN MY HAIR!
and other poems

Go to the Head!

Poems by Ian Bland and Philip Waddell

Hands Up Books

Dedicated to my Mother Irene, Dad John, Sister Debra and
Brother Andrew. Love to all - I.B.
For Denise and Mary Ann - P.W.

British Library Cataloguing in Publication Data.
A catalogue record for this book is available from The British
Library.

ISBN-13: 978-0-9555589-6-2

First Published 2011 by
Hands Up Books
1, New Cottages
Spout Hill
Brantingham
HU15 1QW
East Riding of Yorkshire
Email:handsup@handsup.karoo.co.uk

Printed in the UK by imprintdigital.com

Contents

Making A Meal Of It!   9

I'll Never Fall In Love Again!   10

An Average Poem   12

Don't Forget Your Capital Letters

      And Full Stops!   13

Brazening It Out!   14

A Smile Will Get You Through!   16

The Teachers Are Asleep!   18

Punishment Enough   20

Go To The Head!   22

30 Is The Magic Number   24

Dumb And Mad   26

Dad Can't Cook!   28

Confessions Of A Hungry Young Man   29

The Teatime Rap   31

My Gran - The Nonstop Kiss Machine   32

My Dad's A Rock 'n' Roll Star!   34

Holiday Romance!   36

Picnic List   38

He Said…   39

XI T1 NG   Hobby   40

Football In The Living Room   42

Frightening But True   44

Penalty Pressure!   46

Clearly Guilty   48

The Perfect Halloween Ghoul!   49

The Raving-Mads   51

Sweet Dreams   52

What Am I?   53

Mystery Monster!   54

Cryptic Limerick   55

Looking For The Answer?   56

Minus The Fun!   57

Hat Trick   58

Apt Rewards   60

Tidings   62

Still Not Big Enough   63

The FA Cup Under The Sea   64

The Tale Of The Horrid Thing 66

I'm Sick! 68

The Ostrich 69

ROBOTRON 70

Strength 72

Bull's-eyes 73

Salvaged 74

Jack! 75

Landscape 76

Rose-Coloured Glasses 78

The Optimistic Gardener 79

Making A Meal Of It!

A canny schoolgirl from Dunoon
Explains, 'With a knife, fork and spoon,
Instead of chopsticks,
I could eat in two ticks
This way lunch takes me all afternoon!'

I'll Never Fall In Love Again!

I remember that delicious tingle
The first time I saw Sally Bingle,
Her glasses from the NHS,
A beautiful year 5 princess
With chapped and slightly peeling lips –
My Sally loved a bag of chips

And even though I'm only ten
I'll never fall in love again.

I loved her shirts from M and S,
The way she wore a Tesco dress,
The way she spoke, the way she smiled,
A glance from her would drive me wild –
Then Jason Dodd came on the scene
And stole my girl and wrecked my dream

And even though I'm only ten,
I'll never fall in love again.

With his trainers and his new cagoule
Old Jase thought he was really cool –
All spiky hair and endless smarm
My darling Sal fell for his charm
And now I stand here all alone
While Jason walks my Sally home!

And even though I'm only ten
I'll never fall in love again.

An Average Poem

This is an average poem;
it happens to be ten lines long
and happens to consist of exactly eighty words. Count them.

This line contains the average number of words.

Of its words the word 'the' is the most common
appearing no fewer than five times.
This poem has fifty-six different words.
If you wanted to make bar or pie charts
using the data in this poem you could
though I wouldn't bother... it is just an average poem!

Don't Forget Your Capital Letters And Full Stops!

You can forget to clean your bedroom
Or forget to flush the loo,
You can forget your sister's birthday
And forget your granny's too,
You can forget to get the stains off
When you're made to wash the pots –
But don't forget your capital letters and
FULL STOPS!

You can forget to have a shower
Or forget to clean your teeth,
You can forget to put deodorant
In your armpits – underneath!
You can forget to cut your toenails
And forget to squeeze your spots –
But don't forget your capital letters and
FULL STOPS!

You can forget to weed the garden
Or forget to clean the shed,
You can forget to wash the windows
Or forget to make your bed,
You can forget to take your list out
When you're sent out to the shops –
But don't forget your capital letters and
FULL STOPS!

Brazening It Out!

Teacher :   Why did you hit Jason?
Pupil :   Liam told me to do it!
Teacher :   If Liam told you to jump off a cliff
              would you do it?
Pupil :   If I was going to land on Jason, yes.
Teacher :   Go and stand on the wall!
Pupil :   OK.

A Smile Will Get You Through!

If your teacher always asks you why you're late,
Wear a smile.
If you're asked why all your work is in a state,
Wear a smile.
If they send you to the Head
For a rude word that you said,
Even though you think, I'm dead!
Just wear a smile!

If your test scores are the bottom of the heap,
Wear a smile.
If your lessons make you want to fall asleep,
Wear a smile.
If your teacher is a clown
Who wears a fun-defying frown,
There's no need to be dragged down
Just wear a smile!

If the girls all think you're uglier than sin,
Wear a smile.
If your teacher throws your artwork in the bin,
Wear a smile.
If some nitwit, on your hair,
Dollops glue – do not despair,
Best pretend that you don't care
And wear a smile!

The Teachers Are Asleep!

Shush!
The teachers are asleep –
They're dreaming of the holidays
They're gonna get next week,
They're dreaming about children
Who'll do as they are told,
They're dreaming of the pensions
They'll get when they are old.

Shush!
The teachers are asleep –
They're dreaming of a class of kids
Who hardly ever speak,
They're dreaming of promotion,
They're dreaming they are Heads.
(They dream this dream most every night
When snuggled in their beds.)

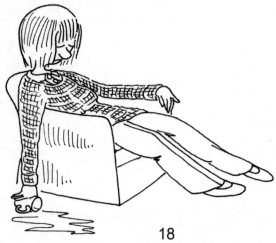

Shush!
The teachers start to snore –
With luck we'll miss their lessons
If no one slams the door!
We can throw away our pencils,
We can be complete disgraces,
We can creep up to our teachers
And pull idiotic faces!

Shush!
The teachers are asleep –
The poor things are so tired
They might snooze until next week.
They're tossing and they're turning,
Sucking thumbs and pulling ears,
There's dribble dribbling down their chins,
They're sliding off their chairs!

Help!
The teachers start to wake –
Their eyelids start to flicker
And their hands begin to shake.
There's going to be trouble,
They arise like the undead,
They're about to hunt for pupils
They can send to see the head!

I didn't make them stay in at playtime,
It was a lot worse than that.

I didn't confiscate their chewing gum,
It was a lot worse than that.

I didn't send them to work in the reception class,
It was a lot worse than that. No.

The last time my class really upset me
I brought *my* mum in!

ial guest:

Rubble

You're always talking, having fun,
You never get your math's work done.
You like to tease and pick a fight,
You never get your spellings right.
Now you're late because you stayed in bed...
Go to the Head!

You run amok, you spit and swear,
You will not sit still in your chair.
You lose your homework, disobey,
You stare and dream the day away.
When told to work you play instead...
Go to the Head!

You pinched his snack and slammed the door,
I think it's time you learnt the score.
You've walked in mud and made a mess,
You've spilt paint down your neighbour's dress.
And I heard that rude word you said...
Go to the Head!

You called out twice and lost your pen
And look – you've ripped your book again!
You've copied answers so don't lie –
And Ben says that you blacked his eye.
And why's the classroom goldfish dead?
Go to the Head!

30 Is The Magic Number

30 sharpened drawing pins
Sit pointedly on chairs,

30 Year 6 hooligans
Come tearing up the stairs,

30 years of teaching hell
Are now almost complete,

30 squawking ten year olds
Are told to take a seat,

30 yelping miscreants
The sweet sound of success,

At 30 thousand decibels
The teacher shouts out

YES!

Dumb And Mad

Mum and Dad seem quite mature
But often, from behind a door,
Will jump to give each other frights
And end up having pillow fights.

Outdoors she's Mum, outdoors he's Dad –
Indoors they're Dumb, indoors they're Mad!

Mum and Dad seem quite well bred
But sometimes round and round their bed
They'll have this childish game of catch
And end up in a tickling match.

Outdoors she's Mum, outdoors he's Dad –
Indoors they're Dumb, indoors they're Mad!

Mum and Dad are Sue and James
But, indoors, they have silly names –
He's Grumpy Bear, she's Soppy Sue –
It's embarrassing but true!

Outdoors she's Mum, outdoors he's Dad –
Indoors they're Dumb, indoors they're Mad!

Mum and Dad don't mess about
Or play around when they are out.
But when they think no one can see
Or hear, they're bigger kids than me!

Outdoors she's Mum, outdoors he's Dad –
Indoors they're Dumb, indoors they're Mad!

Dad Can't Cook!

My dad sings like a pop star
And he can speak in French and Dutch,
He can dig and weed the garden
Though he doesn't do it much,
He can make himself go cross-eyed,
Touch his nose with the tip of his tongue,
But when he tries to cook a meal
It goes very, very wrong!

My dad can juggle oranges
And can climb and swing through trees,
He can jump across our garden pond
With most impressive ease,
He can help me with my homework
When I'm well and truly stuck,
But don't let him cook dinner because
DAD CAN'T COOK!

Confessions Of A Hungry Young Man

When I'm hungry I go to the kitchen
and take it out on food.

In my time
I've beaten eggs
and battered fish.
Gotten into scrapes with toast
and pounded dough.
Duffed plums
and whipped cream.

I've knocked out tasty treats
in kitchen scraps.

And I can't even begin to count the number
of plates I've licked!

The Teatime Rap

As I sat in my room and I played my new game,
My mum got mad then shouted my name,
'It's time that you came down the stairs now Lee,
It's ten past five and it's time for your tea!'
I dawdled downstairs, put my tea on my lap

And I slobbered and I slurped to the teatime rap!
Yes, I slobbered and I slurped to the teatime rap!

With a sausage and an egg and a half baked bun,
I moaned and I said, 'This is not much fun!
I'm bored with this mum, must I eat this food?'
But my mum said, 'Lee! You are far too rude!'
So I turned to the telly and my half chewed bap

And I slobbered and I slurped to the teatime rap!
Yes, I slobbered and I slurped to the teatime rap!

I asked for dessert and my mum said, 'What?'
Cos dessert is the thing that we just ain't got!
'You can chew on an apple or a month old pear!'
But I dreamt of a gateau or a cream éclair
As I picked up my plate and my last few scraps

And I slobbered and I slurped to the teatime rap!
Yes, I slobbered and I slurped to the teatime rap!

My Gran – The Nonstop Kiss Machine

Whenever granny comes to town
She does her best to hunt me down –
And I know when my granny's been
Because she's the nonstop kiss machine

She goes kiss, kiss, kiss, kiss, kiss, kiss, kiss
And she doesn't miss.

It's no use hiding anywhere
My granny's lips will soon appear!
And when I think the worst is done
She takes a breath and carries on

She goes kiss, kiss, kiss, kiss, kiss, kiss, kiss
And she doesn't miss.

It's useless saying I feel ill –
I've tried it but she kisses still!
And even when my cheeks are sore
My gran will kiss a whole lot more

She goes kiss, kiss, kiss, kiss, kiss, kiss, kiss
And she doesn't miss.

And when I try to pull away
My gran will pout and sadly say,
'Give gran a kiss and don't be mean!'
My gran – the nonstop kiss machine

She goes kiss, kiss, kiss, kiss, kiss, kiss, kiss
And she doesn't miss.

My Dad's A Rock'n'Roll Star!
(But only on Friday nights)

On Mondays my dad is so boring
As he gets ready for working again,
He tells us goodbye
As he straightens his tie
Then he dashes to town for his train.

But on Friday nights he's so different,
Then his friends come around with guitars
And dad twangs and he strums
As mum bashes the drums
And my dad and his band are rock stars!

On Wednesdays my dad is so quiet,
He comes home and he kisses my mum –
He watches TV
With his tea on his knee
And won't rest till our homework is done!

But on Friday nights he's a rock star,
He belts rock'n'roll with a roar –
And his friends play along
To each noisy old song
And we clap and we cry out for more!

On Sundays my dad is quite normal,
My mum gives him breakfast in bed –
And then it's a cert
He'll get covered in dirt
As he potters around in the shed.

But on Friday nights he's a rock star,
Then my dad and his band jump and jive –
And the sound that they make
Keeps us all wide awake –
He's the trendiest dad that's alive!

Holiday Romance!

It was the first time
I had been abroad,
My first time out in Spain,
I saw her by the swimming pool
But I didn't know her name.
Her gorgeous hair!
Her pretty face!
I tried to catch her eye,
I really had to talk to her
But I was far too shy!

But then one day
Down on the beach just staring at the view
The girl appeared and boldly said,
'Comment allez vouz?'*
I shot straight up and ran away
And then hid behind a bench,
Some girls are hard enough to face
But this one
She was FRENCH!

* How are you?

Picnic List

Plastic mugs
Snails and slugs
Apple pies
Wasps and flies
Sandwiches
And midges
Hard-boiled eggs
Bitten legs
Ham (tinned)
Rain
Wind

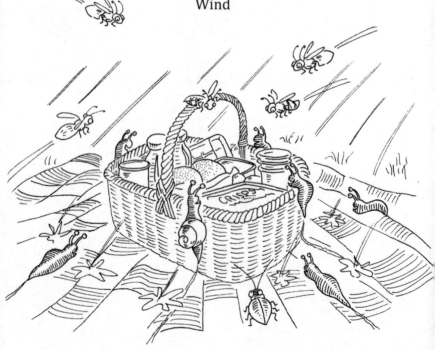

He Said…

He said that friends are always there
That they're honest, loyal and true.

He said that friends will always help
To see the bad times through.

He said that we were kindred
That our friendship was complete.

He said that friends would stay the course
That they would never cheat.

He said, 'It's great that we're best mates.'
And said, 'Here, share my snack!'

I said you must be joking –
I want my girlfriend back!

40

I've just completed my two hundredth jotter.
I'm the world's champion car number plate spotter!

Football In The Living Room

Bounce, Bump, Spin, Bash!
Vase wobble, fall, SMASH!
Shoot, BANG, Blast, BOOM!

FOOTBALL IN THE LIVING ROOM!

Dive, Stretch, Tip, Jerk,
TV hammered – will not work!
Throw, Kick, Swerve, Zoom!

FOOTBALL IN THE LIVING ROOM!

Trap, Aim, Shoot, YES!
Celebrations, GOAL SUCCESS!
Parent trouble, double gloom!

KICKED OUT OF THE LIVING ROOM!

Frightening But True

It's embarrassing, ridiculous
It's frightening, it's sad!
But my mum's a better footballer
Than my brother, me and dad!

Penalty Pressure!

It's a penalty!
The pressure's on
But when I try to score...
I miss my kick
I pirouette
And fall down on the floor!

Clearly Guilty

A mischievous phantom called Clarence
Loved making a sudden appearance.
He thought the trick cool
Till a humourless ghoul
Reported him to his transparents.

The Perfect Halloween Ghoul!

My dad's toupée,
My gran's false teeth,
My sister's skirt,
My brother's briefs,
My granddad's specs,
My old cagoule,
Now look at me –
The perfect ghoul!

The Raving-Mads

Hi!
We've just moved into your neighbourhood.
Our house is just around the bend
where the road gets dippy.
Oh you know it!
Yes the one on Barmy Avenue
with the crazy paving
and the cuckoo clock over the front door.
Anyway we're the Raving-Mads.
I'm Daffy, this is my brother Stu
and she's my sister Dotty.
We were just about to have tea
and wondered if you'd like to join us.
We're having crackers, bananas and fruitcake.
You can't come today?
Oh that's a pity cos most of the time
          we're not all there.

Sweet Dreams

I have the most peculiar dreams when I'm asleep
at night, the worst are full of ghosts and
ghouls and give me quite a fright.
But sometimes I have sweet
dreams when I'm snug
between my
sheets,
the best
are when I'm whisked
away to the wonderland of sweets!
In the land of sweets the streams and rivers flow
with honey, you can eat the liquorice trees for free for
no one asks for money! The lakes are filled with lemonade
and straws are always handy, the cars there run on ginger
beer and on Catherine wheels of candy. The fluffy clouds
are fairground floss and the mud is chocolate mousse, the
hens lay only Easter eggs and the rain is orange juice.
There, mountain snow is whipped ice-cream and
hills are apple crumble – in the land of sweets
you'll never hear a kiddie grumble!
There, bricks are
made
of caramel
and roofs are iced
fruit shortcake and taps
all pour out chocolate (hot) or
cold vanilla milkshake. Once, when I was
enjoying a mattress of marshmallow, I woke to
find my mouth was stuffed with feathers from my pillow!

What Am I?
(Here's a fistful of clues)

Help lender
Mail sender
Warm greeter
Card cheater
Yawn hider
Pen guider
Gift taker
Sign maker
Door knocker
Jaw socker
Tight gripper
Ear clipper
Five scorer
Explorer!

Answer on page 86.

Mystery Monster!
(Fill in the missing word!)

They say...
He's hairy tall and sweaty,
Wields a sharpened curved machete,
Looks a bit like John Paul Getty,
Eats a truck full of spaghetti,
Quite pernickety and petty,
But no one's found him
Y _ _ _ !

Answer on page 86.

Cryptic Limerick

A clever young student from Staines
Solutions to crosswords explains,
'Six letters... Brings down
A smart blow to the crown.
That's easy the answer is _ _ _ _ _ _.'

Answer on page 86.

Looking For The Answer?

Take the letter after L in UNEXPLAINED!
Then the penultimate letter in PUZZLEMENT!
Find the curliest letter in CURIOSITY!
And the foremost letter in WONDERING!
Find the third vowel in NOSINESS!
And the second consonant in PRYING!

Put them all together and
You've found the...?

Answer on page 86.

Minus The Fun!

From 50 take away...

- The Prime Minister's door
- The letters in the alphabet
- The wives of King Henry the VIII

Now add...

- A baker's dozen
- The second highest odd number under 20
- The eyes on a Cyclops

Now divide by...

- The wise monkeys

Did you get it?
(Unlucky!)

Answer on page 86.

Hat Trick

1

It goes BANG with a tap...
Suits a baseball chap...
On a mountain it's made of snow.
Though no eyes - so to speak
It does have a peak!
On a workman's boot it's the toe.

2

Does it play cricket (it sounds like it might)
Or visit the tenpin alley at night?
Paired with a brolly – not now but back then –
It was sported by city gentlemen.

3

It isn't a hat when it's worn by a car
Though a car does look smart with one on it.
It may shade the Queen of the Easter parade
After her beauty has won it.

Answers on page 86.

Apt Rewards

Fortunes -
What singers get
For having worldwide hits.

Pittances -
What miners get
For smashing rocks to bits.

Incomes -
What landlords get
From guests who pay to stay.

Pensions -
What writers get.
(I hope so anyway!)

Poverty -
The lot of those
With empty begging bowls.

Revenue -
What vicars get
For saving sinners' souls.

Tidings

I found a bottle on the beach
Beneath the seabirds' twitter –
It had this message corked inside:
Dispose of – do not litter!

Still Not Big Enough

Imagine you're big.

Not rhinoceros big
Or elephant big
Or dinosaur big
I mean BIG big.

Big enough
For you to need words like
GARGANTUAN, GIGANTIC and IMMENSE
To even begin to describe yourself.

So BIG that when you sing
Your song echoes between continents.

Being that big you'd think
That all before you would quake and quail
But you'd be wrong...
Ask the whale.

The FA Cup Under The Sea

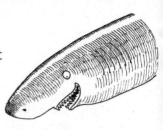

Have you ever seen a dolphin shoot
Or a seahorse foul a sole?
Have you ever seen a dogfish pass
Or a stingray score a goal?

If you haven't seen these things before
You can watch them now for free –
Sit back, relax, enjoy the fun
Of the FA Cup under the sea!

The goalkeeper is a halibut
The defenders are moray eels.
The midfielders are jellyfish
The attackers – prawns and seals!

The referee is an octopus
Who, if he sees a football crime,
Won't hesitate to send you off
With eight cards at a time!

The goalmouth is a sperm whale's jaw
And so to boot one in
You must avoid the razor teeth
Around his mighty grin!

The cheering fans are great white sharks
With smiles, wide and sublime,
Just waiting for the chance
To eat the players at full time.

And the winning team (uneaten)
Get awarded by a guppy
A seashell covered trophy –
The aquatic FA cuppy!

The Tale Of The Horrid Thing

Down in the depths, goes submariners' lore,
Where it's blacker than night – and then blacker some more –
There dwells a Great Thing with two small, sightless eyes...
A creature that further description defies.

It lurked in its lair and whatever sank past
It grabbed at like lightning and gobbled down fast –
It lacked sense of smell and it lacked sense of taste...
Which served it quite well since it mostly gulped waste!

The Great Horrid Thing in its Horrid Thing lair
Didn't think much so it had not a care...
Yet it knew in its heart something missed from its life...
Of course what it missed was a Horrid Thing wife!

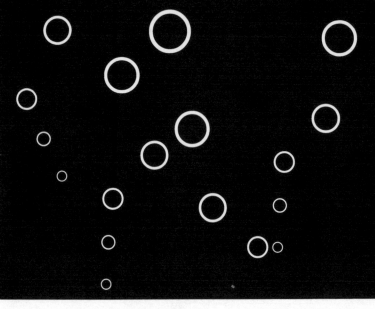

The Horrid Thing took to emitting deep sighs
And sometimes small tears would escape from its eyes –
Till, one day, there sank not the usual muck
But something that promised to change The Thing's luck.

The Horrid Thing fell into what we call love
With the thing that had come from the unknown above –
Its heart skipped a beat when it first sensed the charms
Of the other thing wrapped in its Horrid Thing arms.

The new thing responded in its turn as well
By throbbing and flirting – that's how Thing could tell!
And down in the depths, in the blackness and wet,
It struggled, the new thing, and played hard to get.

Now Thing and his sweetheart are living as one
And Thing's life is filled with such cuddlesome fun!
He's the happiest Thing that the world's never seen…
Since Thing fell in love with his sweet Submarine.

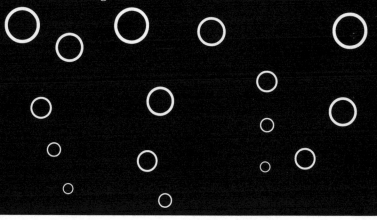

I'm Sick!

I'm sick of this vessel, I'm sick of the crew,
I'm sick of this patch on me eye:
I'm sick of me vest that is hooped white and blue,
I'm sick of the sea and the sky.

I'm sick of me peg leg, I'm sick of me hook,
And I'm sick of seawater tea:
How I'm sick of being a swashbuckling crook!
How I'm sick of piracy!

I'm sick of this hanky I knot round me neck –
There's not really much I can stand:
I'm sick of me parrot and swabbing the deck
And sick of not being on land.

And as for the rations, the mealtimes I dread!
I'm sick of stale bread and grey stew:
And sick of our doctor who's sent me to bed,
He said, 'lad we're all sick of you!'

The Ostrich

The
ostrich
has

A

L
O
N
G

T
H
I
N

N
E
C
K   **That's**
               all about the
               O-S-T-R-E-T-C-H.
And   **So long!**

L L
O O
  N   N
  G   G

    T   T
     H   H
     I   I
   N   N

  L   L
E   E
G   G
S.   S.

ROBOTRON

It's a robot – a monster
And it's gone insane
And it's cavernous mouth
Has just munched up a train!

And – wow – is it angry!
It clomps down the street
Crushing buildings and cars
With its great iron feet.

The police were called out
To shoot ROBOTRON dead,
But their bullets bounced off –
It is too tough for lead!

The army have tried
With a powerful bomb
But ROBOTRON swallowed it –
Gulped it in one!

'There's no way to stop it!'
They screamed as they fled,
'It'll smash up the town
And will leave us all dead!'

And here it comes! ROBOTRON!
Don't stand and stare!
Better run for your life...
To your mum...
Anywhere!

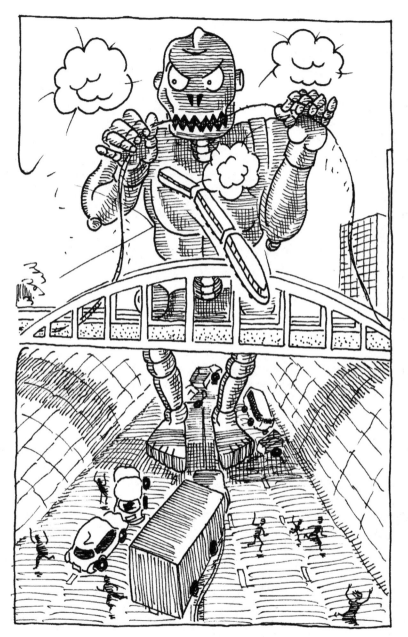

Strength

A sturdy log and a shimmering creek:
One seems strong and the other seems weak.
Logs yield to the axe – creek water, the cup,
But which of the two lifts the other one up?

Bull's-eyes

Still water makes a satisfying target.
Stones dropped into it always score bull's-eyes.

Salvaged

This
poem
is orderly, tidy, organised.
There's a place for every letter and every letter's in its place. There's a place for every word and every word is in its place. There's a place for every sentence and every sentence is in its place. It wasn't launched like this, at first it was just flotsam in my head but now I've salvaged it and made it shipshape.

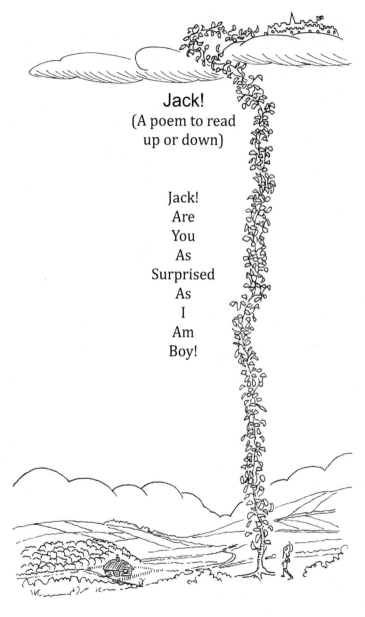

Jack!
(A poem to read up or down)

Jack!
Are
You
As
Surprised
As
I
Am
Boy!

Landscape

In the distance –
As far as the eye can see,
Herds of houses
Where zebra used to be.

In the highways –
As far as the eye can see,
Snorting traffic
Where rhinos used to be.

Round the lakeside –
As far as the eye can see,
Flocks of diggers
Where plovers used to be.

By the river –
As far as the eye can see,
Basking rubbish
Where hippos used to be.

Rose-Coloured Glasses

Some say the world is sad and grey
I beg to disagree,
Clear skies and smiling faces
Are the only ones I see.

Some say the world's a hopeless case
That isn't what I think,
I bet you too would take my view
If your lenses were pink.

The Optimistic Gardener

This year he planted

Marigolds
Carnations
Poppies
and Petunias.

As usual
everything's come up roses.

Ian's Poems

I'll Never Fall In Love Again!   10

Don't Forget Your Capital Letters

       And Full Stops!   13

Brazening It Out!   14

A Smile Will Get You Through!   16

The Teachers Are Asleep!   18

Punishment Enough   20

Go To The Head!   22

30 Is The Magic Number   24

Dad Can't Cook!   28

The Teatime Rap   31

My Gran - The Nonstop Kiss Machine   32

My Dad's A Rock 'n' Roll Star!   34

Holiday Romance!   36

He Said…   39

Football In The Living Room   42

Frightening But True   44

Penalty Pressure!   46

The Perfect Halloween Ghoul!   49

Sweet Dreams   52

Mystery Monster!   54

Looking For The Answer?   56

Minus The Fun!   57

The FA Cup Under The Sea   64

ROBOTRON   70

Philip's Poems

Making A Meal Of It! 9

An Average Poem 12

Dumb And Mad 26

Confessions Of A Hungry Young Man 29

Picnic List 38

XI T1 NG Hobby 40

Clearly Guilty 48

The Raving-Mads 51

What Am I? 53

Cryptic Limerick 55

Hat Trick 58

Apt Rewards 60

Tidings 62

Still Not Big Enough 63

The Tale Of The Horrid Thing 66

I'm Sick! 68

The Ostrich 69

Strength 72

Bull's-eyes 73

Salvaged   74

Jack!   75

Landscape   76

Rose-Coloured Glasses   78

The Optimistic Gardener   79

Acknowledgements

Ian's Poems:

'Brazening It Out!' and 'Punishment Enough' first published in *How To Survive School*, David Harmer, Macmillan's Children's Books, 2006.

'Holiday Romance!' first published in *Are we nearly there yet?*, Brian Moses, Macmillan's Children's Books, 2002.

'Frightening But True' and 'Penalty Pressure!' first published in *The World at our Feet*, Paul Cookson, Macmillan's Children's Books, 2010.

'Sweet Dreams' first published in *What Shape is a Poem?*, Paul Cookson, Macmillan's Children's Books, 2002.

'Looking For The Answer?' and 'Minus The Fun!' first published in *The Trying Flapeze and other Puzzle Poems*, John Foster/Tony Ross, OUP, 2004.

Philip's Poems:

'An Average Poem' first published in *Read Me At School*, Gaby Morgan, Macmillan's Children's Books, 2009.

'What Am I?' first published in *The Secret Life Of Pants And Other Brilliant New Poems*, Roger Stevens, A & C Black, 2006.

'Salvaged' first published in *The Upside Down Frown*, Andrew Fusek Peters, Wayland Publishers Ltd, 1999.

Answers to riddles:

What Am I?   A Hand
Mystery Monster!   Yeti
Cryptic Limerick   Brains
Looking For The Answer?   ANSWER
Minus The Fun!   13
Hat Trick   1) Cap 2) Bowler 3) Bonnet